Jessica Swenson

The Paleo Challenge

7 Proven Steps to Lose Weight

D1531106

Table of Contents

Do you want to lose weight, look great and feel fantastic?

Now, with **The Paleo Challenge: 7 Proven Steps to Lose Weight** you can do just that in next to no time.

The Paleo diet is a fairly new idea which is gathering momentum as one of the best and healthiest diets available. It concentrates on eating foods that were available to hunter-gatherer Palaeolithic peoples, hence the name, and it removes the unnatural processed foods which have become commonplace.

Inside this book you will discover a Paleo challenge which will help you lose weight with:

- 7 days of breakfast recipes
- 7 days of lunch recipes
- 7 days of dinner recipes
- paleo diet 3 month food journal
- shopping list for fool paleo diet.

This amazing healthy eating diet plan focuses on eating quality natural foods which our bodies were designed to digest while on the move. It is a proven method of losing weight and completely avoids the risks which can sometimes be posed by some modern 'fad' diets.

Get your copy of **The Paleo Challenge** today! A healthier and leaner you is waiting.

Introduction

Are you struggling to lose weight? Have you tried various diets without success? Then this book on Paleo diet can help you to achieve your weight loss goals. T

he Paleo diet helps you to lose fat, and avoid heart disease, diabetes, cancer, Alzheimer's and a host of other diseases. Going Paleo helps you look, feel and perform your best. Paleo incorporates foods that our bodies were designed to eat.

High protein, low carb, healthy fat and full of wholesome, natural foods; the Paleo diet has taken the world by storm and changed millions of lives for better.

The book includes fresh, creative, flavorsome, mouthwatering Paleo recipes. You don't have to worry about the diet being expensive; the book will show you how to make delicious dishes with simple and accessible ingredients.

The Paleo diet is the only diet proven by nature to keep you naturally slim, provide maximum energy, and fight disease while you enjoy satisfying meals. You will love the Paleo diet, and it will become an integral part of your life. If you are planning to transition to the Paleo diet soon, then this Paleo diet book is for you.

The Reason Why You Lose Weight On The Paleo Diet

Commonly used word "Paleo" is an abbreviation of *Paleolithic*, which refers to the Paleolithic Era approximately 2.5 million years ago. Hence, the Paleo diet is based on eating foods that have been available to our hunter-gather Paleolithic ancestors. The diet strictly avoids all forms of modern foods that would have been unavailable in the Paleolithic Era.

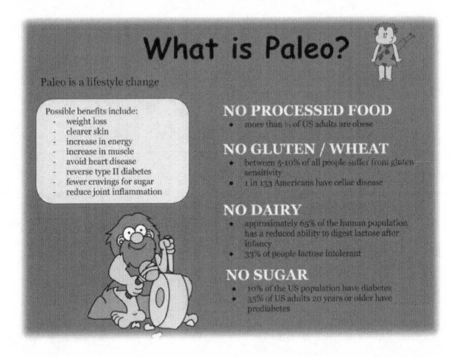

Fundamentally, the Paleo diet is a healthy eating diet plan that focuses on only eating quality natural foods, and avoiding unhealthy processed foods that offer no nutritional value to our bodies.

Celebrities That Have Been Rumoured To Follow The Paleo Diet

- Megan Fox
- Uma Thurman
- Jessica Biel
- Miley Cyrus
- Tom Jones
- Matthew McConaughey
- Andrew Flintoff

The foods included in the Paleo diet are the primeval foods our bodies were designed to digest while on the move and foods excluded are those that only included in our diet as a result of modern-day cultivation and farming practices.

Why You Lose Weight On the Paleo Diet

With Paleo, you lower your carbohydrate intake and increase your fat intake, so your body learns to burn fat for fuel. A standard diet that is high in carbs leads to raised insulin levels, which causes your body to store fat. This creates an unhealthy cycle – fat gets stored, your body craves for more carbs for fuel and consuming more carb leads to more fat storage and weight gain.

With Paleo, you avoid this vicious cycle and lose weight. Besides, your body adapts to burning fat for energy and your workouts become much more efficient. So you don't need long exercise sessions, and you lose extra body fat and get that lean physique you always wanted.

Paleo TakeOver

EAT IT	STAY AWAY
MEATS: chicken, duck, turkey, rabbit, pork tenderloin, pork chops, lamb, steak, bacon, grass fed beef, ground beef, venison, buffalo, goat	**DAIRY:** cheese, butter, cottage cheese, milk, creamer, powder milk, yogurt, pudding, cream cheese, frozen yogurt, ice cream
FISH: shrimp, clams, lobster, mussels, oysters, salmon	**DRINKS:** sodas, fruit juice, energy drinks, alcohol (if you must consume alcohol, gin, rum, tequila and red wine are preferable)
EGGS: duck, chicken, goose, quail, caviar, roe	**GRAINS:** cereal, bread, crackers, oatmeal, corn, wheat products

EAT IT	STAY AWAY
VEGETABLES: artichokes, asparagus, avocado, broccoli, brussels sprouts, cabbage, carrots, celery, egg-plant, onions, peppers, spinach, zuchinni	**LEGUMES:** beans, peas, soybean, soybean products, chickpeas, snowpeas, sugar snap peas, peanuts, lentils, miso, tofu
OILS + FATS: avocado oil, coconut oil, macadamia oil, olive oil, grass fed butter	**FATTY MEATS:** hot-dogs, spam, low-quality and processed meats
NUTS: almonds, cashews, pine nuts, pumpkin seeds, pecans, hazelnuts, sunflower seeds, macadamia nuts, walnuts	**SWEETS:** sugars, sweeteners, candy, honey (unless raw in small amounts)
FRUITS: apples, avocados, blueberries, blackberries, strawberries, raspberries, grapes, plums, peaches, papaya, lemon, lime, pineapple, cantaloupe, figs, oranges, bananas, watermelon	**STARCHY VEGGIES:** potatoes, yucca, butternut squash, acorn squash, yams, beets

The Benefits of The Paleo Diet and Criticism of The Diet

The benefits of the Paleo diet

The Paleo diet provides you so many health benefits, including:

- **Sustained weight loss:** Most dieters experience body fat loss and muscle growth when following the Paleo diet and doing exercise regularly.
- **The diet includes unprocessed, real food:** The Paleo diet includes unprocessed, real foods. With the diet, you eliminate a whole range of additives, preservatives, coloring, artificial flavoring, hidden sugars, and sodium. Not only you lose weight, but also you become healthier.
- **The diet is rich in nutrients:** The Paleo diet eliminates processed carbs and supplements it with healthy fats, fruits, vegetables, berries, seeds, and nuts. All of these are full of vitamins and minerals.
- **Reduced bloat:** The diet provides your body enough fiber, which improves digestion. Also, the diet improves the gut flora and keeps it healthy.
- **You feel less hungry:** Unlike carb rich foods, meals that include fat and protein are very satiating. The slow releasing energy from low GI carbs, fat and protein help your body to stay active all day without feeling excessively hungry.

o **Includes healthy fats:** The Paleo diet includes healthy fats from sources such as coconuts, butter, ghee, seafood, poultry, and grass-fed meat. Healthy fats are needed reducing systemic inflammation and maintaining healthy skin, brain function, and healthy arteries.

Criticisms of the Paleo diet

Despite the benefits, there are a few criticisms of the Paleo diet, including

o **There is no standard Paleo diet:** When eating Paleo, we follow the diet of our hunter-gatherer ancestors. However, our ancestors lived in different parts of the world, including islands, coastal areas, arctic condition or desert areas. **Different part of the world offers different types of foods, and this is why there is no standard Paleo diet.**

o **The diet is harder to follow:** To strictly follow the Paleo diet, you have to cook. However, we are living a busy life these days and have no time to cook, and this makes the diet hard to follow.

o **The diet is expensive:** The Paleo diet includes unprocessed, natural, nutrient dense foods, which are expensive.

o **You have to follow strictly to get the result:** To get the benefit of the diet, you have to follow it strictly; otherwise, the diet won't work.

Now we are going to discuss detail menu of the Paleo diet for 7 days. Starting with 7 days breakfast recipes, then 7 days lunch recipes and lastly 7 days dinner recipes.

Breakfast Recipes

Omelet with Avocado and Pico De Gallo

Ingredients for 1 serving

- o Cooking spray
- o Egg – 1 large
- o Egg white – 1 large

- Salt and pepper to taste
- Avocado – 1 ounce, sliced
- Pico de gallo – 2 tablespoons

Method

1. In a small bowl, beat the egg white and egg. Season with salt and pepper.
2. Heat a nonstick skillet over medium heat and spray oil-cooking spray.
3. Pour the eggs and cook for 2 to 3 minutes, or until set.
4. Transfer to a plate.
5. Top with pico de gallo and avocado and enjoy.

Nutrition Information Per Serving

- Calories : 140
- Total fat : 9g
- Carbohydrate : 4g
- Protein : 11g

Turkey Sausage Breakfast Patties

Ingredients for 6 servings

- o Cooking spray
- o Olive oil – 1 tsp.
- o Onion – 1 small, diced small
- o Garlic – 1 large clove, chopped
- o Kosher salt and black pepper to taste
- o Fennel seed – 1 tsp.
- o Lean ground turkey – 1 lb. 93%
- o Red wine vinegar – 1 tbsp.

- o   Chopped chives – 1 tbsp.
- o   Paprika – ¾ tsp.
- o   Pinch nutmeg
- o   Pinch raw sugar

Method

1. Over medium-low heat, heat a medium skillet.
2. Then add oil, garlic and onion. Stir and cook until onion is translucent about 5 minutes. If needed, lower the heat.
3. Add fennel and cook for 1 minute or until fragrant and toasted.
4. Place the mixture in a medium bowl.
5. Add sugar, nutmeg, paprika, chives, red wine vinegar and ground turkey to the bowl with onion-fennel mixture. Mix well with a fork.
6. Make 6 even patties and place on a parchment paper.
7. Spray a skillet with cooking spray and place over medium-low heat.
8. Brown turkey patties in the hot pan in two batches.
9. Cook 3 minutes on each side.
10. Once the patties get a browned crust on each side; lower the heat and cover.
11. Continue to cook until the internal temperature reaches 165F.
12. Remove and cook the second batch.

Nutrition Information Per Serving

- o   Calories : 134
- o   Total fat : 6g
- o   Carbohydrate : 3g
- o   Protein : 15g

Sweet Potato Chicken Hash with Eggs

Ingredients for 4 servings

- Olive oil – 1 tbsp.
- Onion – 1 medium, chopped
- Peeled sweet potatoes – 10 ounces, diced into ½-inch pieces
- Fresh thyme – 2 tsp.
- Garlic powder – ½ tsp.
- Paprika – ¼ tsp.

- Leftover chicken breasts – 8 oz. diced into ½-inch pieces
- Eggs – 4 large
- Fresh chopped chives – 1 tbsp.

Method

1. Heat a oven safe skillet over medium heat.
2. Add the oil and onions and cook for 5 minutes, or until the onions are golden.
3. Add the sweet potatoes, paprika, garlic powder, thyme, black pepper and ¾ tsp. salt.
4. Add about 3 tbsp. water, cover and cook sweet potatoes on medium-low heat for 8 to 12 minutes or until crisp and tender. Stir occasionally.
5. Add the chicken to the skillet and cook for a couple of minutes, uncovered.
6. Make 4 wells in the hash and then crack 1 egg into each well.
7. Season with salt, pepper, and cover.
8. Cook for 5 to 7 minutes, or until whites are set, and yolks are runny.
9. Top with fresh herbs.

Nutrition Information Per Serving

- Calories : 265
- Total fat : 10g
- Carbohydrate : 18g
- Protein : 25g

Baked Eggs with Wilted Baby Spinach

Ingredients for 4 servings

- Olive oil – 2 tsp.
- Diced shallots – ¼ cup
- Baby spinach – 1 ½ lb. large stems, removed
- Eggs – 4 large
- Salt and pepper to taste
- Shredded Asiago cheese – 2 tbsp.
- Baking spray

Method

1. Preheat the oven to 400F. Lightly spray four oven-safe dishes with cooking spray.
2. Heat a large skillet over medium-low heat.
3. Add oil and cook shallots for 2 to 3 minutes.
4. Add spinach, season with salt and pepper and cook for 2 to 3 minutes, or until wilts. Mix in the cheese and remove from heat.
5. Split the cooked spinach between the oven-safe dishes. Then make a well in the middle of each.
6. On each dish, break an egg and season with salt and pepper.
7. Place the dishes on one rimmed baking sheet and cook at least 17 minutes, or until the yolks soft in the center, but firm around the edges and whites are set.

Nutrition Information Per Serving

o   Calories : 152.5
o   Total fat : 9.3g
o   Carbohydrate : 7.9g
o   Protein : 12.2g

Pumpkin Pie Oatmeal Breakfast Brûlée

Ingredients for 1 serving

- Cooked steel cutor regular oatmeal – 1 cup
- Pumpkin puree – 2 tbsp.
- Pure maple syrup – 1 tsp.
- Vanilla extract – ¼ tsp.
- Pumpkin pie spice – ¼ tsp.
- Pinch of sea salt
- Pecans – 1 tbsp. chopped
- Coconut sugar – ½ tsp.

- o Almond milk or coconut milk – optional
- o Collagen peptides – 1 scoop, optional

Method

1. Place a small saucepan over medium heat.
2. Combine cooked oatmeal, sea salt, pumpkin spice, vanilla, maple syrup, and pumpkin puree.
3. Mix and heat for 3 to 4 minutes, then add pecans. Remove from the heat.
4. Set oven to broil.
5. Place oatmeal in an oven-safe bowl and sprinkle with coconut sugar.
6. Broil until brown on top, about 1 minute.
7. Top with additional milk and pecans if desired.

Nutrition Information Per Serving

- o Calories : 241
- o Total fat : 8g
- o Carbohydrate : 37g
- o Protein : 6g

Baked Eggs in Harissa Spice

Ingredients for 4 servings

- Olive oil – ½ tsp.
- Minced red onion – 2 tbsp.
- Petite tomatoes – 14.5 oz. can
- Prepared Harissa – 2 tbsp.
- Eggs – 4 large
- Salt and pepper to taste
- Fresh chopped parsley or chives – 1 tsp.

Method

1. Heat a large skillet over medium heat.
2. Add the oil and onion and sauté for 2 to 3 minutes, or until golden.
3. Add harissa, tomatoes, and season with salt and pepper.
4. Increase heat to medium-high and simmer for 3 to 4 minutes, or until the liquid reduces a bit.
5. Reduce the heat to medium-low, then add the eggs. Season with salt and pepper and cover.
6. Cook for 5 minutes, or until the top of the eggs are set.
7. Top with chopped parsley or chives.

Nutrition Information Per Serving

- Calories : 102.5
- Total fat : 5g
- Carbohydrate : 5g
- Protein : 7g

Breakfast Muffins

Ingredients for 6 servings

- Ghee – 3 tbsp.
- Frank's red hot sauce – 3 tbsp.
- Coconut aminos – 1 tbsp.
- Cayenne pepper – 1/8 tsp.
- Red bell pepper – ½, diced small
- Green onions – 3 (white and green parts, chopped)
- Spinach – 2 cups, chopped
- Cooked chicken – 1 cup, cubed
- Whole eggs – 8

- o   Salt – ½ tsp.
- o   Black pepper – ¼ tsp.

Method

1. Preheat the oven to 350F.
2. Grease the wells of a 12-cup muffin pan.
3. To make the sauce: melt 2 ½ tbsp. ghee in a small saucepan. Whisk in coconut aminos, hot sauce, and cayenne pepper until combined. Remove from heat and set aside.
4. Melt remaining ½ tbsp. ghee in a skillet over medium-high heat. Sauté onion and bell pepper for 5 minutes, or until slightly softened.
5. Turn off heat. Add cooked chicken, spinach and sauce to onions and peppers. Sit to combine.
6. Divide the chicken-vegetable mixture evenly between wells of the muffin pan.
7. Beat egg with salt and pepper in a bowl and pour over vegetable mixture.
8. Bake at 350F until eggs are set, and a toothpick inserted in the middle comes out clean, about 18 to 20 minutes.
9. Remove from pan and serve.

Nutrition Information Per Serving (2 muffins)

- o   Calories : 207
- o   Total fat : 14g
- o   Carbohydrate : 3g
- o   Protein : 16g

Lunch Recipes
Sloppy Joe Baked Sweet Potatoes

Ingredients for 4 servings

- o Sweet potatoes – 4 medium, washed and dried (7 oz. each)
- o Lean ground beef – ½ lb. 93%
- o Seasoned salt – 1 tsp.
- o Chopped carrot – 1/3 cup
- o Chopped onion – 1/3 cup
- o Chopped mushrooms – 1/3 cup

- Chopped red bell pepper – 2 tbsp.
- Garlic – 1 clove, minced
- Red wine vinegar – ½ tbsp.
- Worcestershire sauce – ½ tbsp.
- Tomato sauce – 8 oz. can
- Tomato paste – 2 tsp.
- Water – 1/3 cup
- Chopped scallion -1, for garnish

Method

1. Poke holes all over the sweet potatoes with a fork. Then cook in an oven or slow cooker until tender.
2. Heat a medium skillet over medium-high heat.
3. Add the meat, season with steak seasoning and cook. Break up the meat into small pieces.
4. Add the onion, red peppers, mushrooms, carrots, and garlic to the skillet.
5. Lower the heat to medium. Then add Worcestershire sauce and red wine vinegar. Cook for 5 minutes.
6. Add water, tomato paste, and sauce to the skillet. Stir to combine.
7. Cover and cook for 15 to 20 minutes, or until carrots are tender.
8. Cut sweet potatoes open, then sprinkle with salt.
9. Top each with ½ cup of meat and garnish with scallion.

Nutrition Information Per Serving

- Calories : 259
- Total fat : 4g
- Carbohydrate : 40g
- Protein : 15.5g

Cauliflower Soup with Roasted Brussels Sprouts

Ingredients for 4 servings

- o Cooking spray
- o Cauliflower florets – 16 oz.
- o Brussels sprouts – 16 oz. halved
- o Olive oil – 2 tbsp.
- o Butter – 1 tsp.
- o Chopped shallots – ½ cup
- o Vegetable broth – 3 ½ cups
- o Kosher salt – ¾ tsp.

- o Black pepper to taste

Method

1. Preheat the oven to 450F.
2. Line a large baking sheet with foil, then spray with oil.
3. Place the Brussels and cauliflower on the baking sheet (cut side down).
4. Drizzle with oil and roast on the lower part of the oven until slightly browned, about 25 minutes.
5. Meanwhile, in a large saucepan, melt the butter over low heat and add the shallots. Cook for 5 minutes, or until translucent.
6. Add the broth and simmer for 5 minutes.
7. Close the oven door. Set aside about 1 cup of roasted vegetables.
8. Transfer the rest to the pot and simmer for 2 minutes.
9. In a blender, blend until smooth in batches.
10. Serve in 4 bowls top with fresh black pepper and roasted vegetables.

Nutrition Information Per Serving

- o Calories : 173
- o Total fat : 8g
- o Carbohydrate : 22g
- o Protein : 6.5g

Turkey Taco Lettuce Wraps

Ingredients for 4 servings

- Lean ground turkey – 1.3 lbs. 93%
- Garlic powder – 1 tsp.
- Cumin – 1 tsp.
- Salt – 1 tsp.
- Chili powder – 1 tsp.
- Paprika – 1 tsp.
- Oregano - ½ tsp.
- Small onion – ½, minced

- ○ Bell pepper – 2 tbsp. minced
- ○ Water – ¾ cup
- ○ Tomato sauce – 4 oz. can
- ○ Iceberg lettuce leaves – 8 large
- ○ Shredded reduced fat cheddar – ½ cup, optional

Method

1. In a large skillet, brown turkey and break it into smaller pieces.
2. Once browned, add dry seasoning and mix well.
3. Add tomato sauce, water, onion, pepper, and cover. Simmer for 20 minutes.
4. Divide the meat among 8 leaves and top with cheese.

Nutrition Information Per Serving

- ○ Calories : 255
- ○ Total fat : 11g
- ○ Carbohydrate : 6g
- ○ Protein : 30g

Canned Tuna Ceviche

Ingredients for 2 servings

- o   Minced red onion – 2 tbsp.
- o   Limes – 1 or 2
- o   Kosher salt and black pepper as needed
- o   Olive oil – 1 tsp.
- o   Chunk white albacore tuna packed in water - 1 (7 oz.) can, drained
- o   Seeded plum tomato – 1 medium, finely diced
- o   Chopped cilantro – 2 tbsp.
- o   Jalapeno – 1, minced
- o   Tabasco sauce – 3 drops, optional
- o   Sliced avocado – 2 oz.

Method

1. In a bowl, combine olive oil, juice of 1 lime, a pinch of kosher salt and red onion.
2. Mix in the tabasco, tomato, drained tuna, jalapeno, and chopped cilantro. Taste and adjust seasoning.
3. Cover and marinate in the refrigerator for minimum 20 minutes.
4. Top with fresh sliced avocado and serve.

Nutrition Information Per Serving

- Calories : 153
- Total fat : 8g
- Carbohydrate : 9g
- Protein : 15g

California Grilled Chicken with Vinaigrette Dressing

Ingredients for 4 servings

- o Grilled chicken breast – 12 oz. (about 1 lb. raw)
- o Diced avocado – 1 cup
- o Diced mango – 1 cup
- o Diced red onion – 2 tbsp.
- o Baby red butter lettuce – 6 cups

For the vinaigrette

- o Olive oil – 2 tbsp.
- o White balsamic vinegar – 2 tbsp.

o   Salt and fresh pepper to taste

Method

1. In a bowl, whisk vinaigrette ingredients and set aside.
2. Toss red onion, chicken, mango and avocado together.
3. Divide baby greens into 4 small dishes.
4. Top with avocado-chicken mixture and drizzle half the dressing or top.
5. Serve with the rest of the dressing.

Nutrition Information Per Serving

o   Calories : 258
o   Total fat : 14.6g
o   Carbohydrate : 12.2g
o   Protein : 20.7g

Blueberry Chicken Salad

Ingredients for 4 or 5

- o Boneless, skinless chicken breasts – 2 (cooked, cooled and cubed)
- o Fresh blueberries – ½ cup
- o Diced celery – ¼ cup
- o Diced red onion – ¼ cup
- o Chopped walnuts – 3 tbsp.
- o Fresh rosemary leaves – 1 tbsp. chopped
- o Sea salt – ¼ tsp.

- Black pepper – 1/8 tsp.
- Homemade mayo – ¼ cup

Method

1. To make the salad: in a bowl, combine cooked chicken and remaining ingredients in a bowl.
2. Add mayo and stir to combine.
3. Serve with cucumber slices, or over a bed of mixed greens.

Nutrition Information Per Serving

- Calories : 264
- Total fat : 17.4g
- Carbohydrate : 2g
- Protein : 22g

Steak Kebabs with Chimichurri

Ingredients for 6 servings (1 skewers each)

- o Beef – 1 ¼ pounds (cut into 1-inch cubes)
- o Fresh ground pepper to taste
- o Kosher salt – 1 ¼ tsp.
- o Red onion – 1 large, cut into large chunks
- o Cherry tomatoes – 18
- o Bamboo skewers – 6, soaked in water for 1 hour

For the chimichurri sauce

- o Finely chopped parsley – 2 tbsp. packed

- Chopped cilantro – 2 tbsp. packed
- Red onion – 2 tbsp. finely chopped
- Garlic – 1 clove, minced
- Extra virgin olive oil – 2 tbsp.
- Apple cider vinegar – 2 tbsp.
- Water – 1 tbsp.
- Kosher salt – ¼ tsp.
- Fresh black pepper – 1/8 tsp.
- Crushed red pepper flakes – 1/8 tsp.

Method

1. Season the meat with salt and pepper.
2. For the sauce: in a bowl, combine olive oil, salt, vinegar, and red onion and set aside for 5 minutes.
3. Now add the remaining ingredients and keep in the refrigerator until ready to use.
4. Onto the skewers, place the beef, onions, and tomatoes.
5. Prepare the grill on high heat.
6. Grill the steaks 2 to 3 minutes per side for medium-rare.
7. Transfer steaks to a platter and top with chimichurri sauce.

Nutrition Information Per Serving

- Calories : 219
- Total fat : 13g
- Carbohydrate : 5.5g
- Protein : 20g

Dinner Recipes
Garlic Shrimp with Tomatoes

Ingredients for 4 servings

- Jumbo shrimp – 1 ¼ lbs. (peeled and deveined)
- Extra virgin olive oil – 1 tsp.
- Red bell pepper – 1, sliced thin
- Thinly sliced scallions – 4, white and green parts separated
- Cilantro – ½ cup
- Garlic – 4 cloves, minced
- Kosher salt to taste
- Crushed red pepper flakes – ½ tsp.
- Diced tomatoes – 14.5 oz. can
- Light coconut milk – 14 oz. can (50% less fat)
- Lime – ½, squeezed

Method

1. Heat oil in a medium pot over low heat. Add red peppers and sauté for 4 minutes, or until soft. Add garlic, red pepper flakes ¼ cup cilantro and scallion whites. Cook for 1 minute.
2. Add coconut milk, tomatoes and salt to taste. Cover and simmer on low heat for 10 minutes to thicken the sauce.
3. Add shrimp and cook for 5 minutes. Add lime juice.
4. Divide among 4 bowls and top with cilantro and scallions.

Nutrition Information Per Serving

- o   Calories : 261
- o   Total fat : 10g
- o   Carbohydrate : 10g
- o   Protein : 30g

Thai Coconut Shrimp Curry

Ingredients for 4 servings

- o Oil – 1 tsp.
- o Chopped scallions – 4, whites and greens separated
- o Thai red curry paste – 1 tbsp.
- o Garlic – 2 cloves, minced
- o Shrimp – 1 lb. peeled and deveined
- o Light coconut milk – 6 oz.
- o Fish sauce – 2 tsp.
- o Fresh cilantro – ¼ cup, chopped
- o Salt to taste

Method

1. Heat oil over medium-high heat in a large skillet.
2. Add scallion whites and curry paste and sauté for 1 minute.
3. Add garlic and shrimp. Season with salt and cook for 2 minutes.
4. Add fish sauce and coconut milk, mix well. Simmer until shrimp is cooked through, about 2 to 3 minutes.
5. Remove from heat; mix in cilantro and scallion greens.
6. Serve over rice.

Nutrition Information Per Serving

- Calories : 135
- Total fat : 4.4g
- Carbohydrate : 4.7g
- Protein : 18.5g

Spiced Flounder with Tomatoes

Ingredients for 4 servings

- Olive oil – 1 tsp.
- Flounder fillets – 4 (6 oz.) pieces
- Onion – ¾ cup, chopped
- Garlic – 2 cloves, minced
- Diced green bell pepper – ¾ cup
- Tomatoes – 2 ½ cups, chopped
- Cajun spice seasoning – 1 tbsp.

Method

1. In a deep skillet, heat olive oil over medium heat. Cook onion and garlic until soft.

2. Add spices, peppers, and tomatoes. Cook and stir for 2 to 3 minutes, or until tomatoes are soft.
3. Place fillets in the sauce. Cover and cook on medium heat for 12 to 15 minutes, or until fish flakes easily.
4. Place fish on plate and spoon sauce on top.
5. Serve.

Nutrition Information Per Serving

- Calories : 205.8
- Total fat : 3.8g
- Carbohydrate : 10.2g
- Protein : 33.2g

Beef, Cabbage, and Tomato Soup

Ingredients for 7 servings

- o   Lean ground beef – 1 lb. 90%
- o   Kosher salt – 1-1/2 tsp.
- o   Diced onion – ½ cup
- o   Diced celery – ½ cup
- o   Diced carrot – ½ cup
- o   Diced tomatoes – 28 oz. can
- o   Chopped green cabbage – 5 cups
- o   Homemade beef stock – 4 cups

o   Bay leaves – 2

Method

1. Heat a large pot over medium-high heat.
2. Spray with oil and add ground beef. Season with salt and pepper and cook for 3 to 4 minutes, or until browned. Break the meat into smaller pieces.
3. When browned, add carrots, celery, and onion and sauté for 5 minutes.
4. Add the bay leaves, beef stock, cabbage, and tomatoes. Cook on low heat for 40 minutes, covered.

Nutrition Information Per Serving

o   Calories : 181
o   Total fat : 6g
o   Carbohydrate : 14g
o   Protein : 15.5g

Cuban Picadillo

Ingredients for 6 servings

- o   Onion – ½ chopped large
- o   Garlic – 2 cloves, minced
- o   Chopped tomato – 1
- o   Pepper – ½, finely chopped
- o   Cilantro – 2 tbsp.
- o   Lean ground beef – 1 -1/2 lb. 93%
- o   Tomato sauce – ½ can (4 oz.)
- o   Kosher salt

- ○ Fresh ground pepper
- ○ Ground cumin – 1 tsp.
- ○ Bay leaf – 1 or 2
- ○ Alcaparrado or green olives – 2 tbsp.

Method

1. In a large pan, brown meat on high heat. Break up the meat into smaller pieces and season with salt and pepper. Drain all juice from pan, when meat is no longer pink.
2. Meanwhile, chop cilantro, tomato, pepper, garlic and onion.
3. Add to the meat and continue to cook on low heat.
4. Add alcaparrado, bay leaf, cumin and more salt according to taste.
5. Add ¼ cup of water and tomato sauce and mix well.
6. Lower heat and simmer 20 minutes, covered.

Nutrition Information Per Serving

- ○ Calories : 207
- ○ Total fat : 8.5g
- ○ Carbohydrate : 5g
- ○ Protein : 25g

Steak with Tomatoes

Ingredients for 6 servings

- o   Sirloin tip steak - 1 ½ lbs. sliced very thin
- o   Salt to taste
- o   Tomatoes – 2 medium, chopped
- o   Onion – 1 medium, chopped
- o   Olive oil – 4 tsp.
- o   Garlic powder to taste
- o   Cumin to taste

Method

1. Season steak with salt and pepper.
2. Heat a frying pan and add 2 tsp oil. Add ½ of the steak in hot oil and cook each side less than a minute. Set aside.

3. Add another teaspoon of oil and cook the other half of the steak. Set aside.
4. Lower heat to medium and 1-teaspoon oil and add the onions.
5. Cook for 2 minutes, then add the tomatoes. Add cumin, season with salt and pepper. Lower heat to medium-low.
6. Add ¼ cup water and create a sauce by simmering a few minutes. Taste and adjust seasoning.
7. Add the steak with the dripping. Mix well and remove from heat.
8. Serve over rice.

Nutrition Information Per Serving

o   Calories : 182.9
o   Total fat : 7.2g
o   Carbohydrate : 3g
o   Protein : 25.2g

Skillet Steak with Mushrooms and Onions

Ingredients for 4 servings

- o   Thin sliced beef round – ½ lb.
- o   Large onion – ½, sliced into rings
- o   Olive oil – ½ tsp.
- o   Sliced mushrooms – 8 oz.
- o   Cooking spray
- o   Salt and pepper to taste
- o   Garlic powder to taste

Method

1. Season beef with garlic powder, salt, and pepper to taste.
2. Heat a large skillet over high heat.

3. Spray with cooking spray and cook half of the beef for 1 minute. Then flip and cook the other side for 30 seconds. Set aside in a large dish and repeat with the remaining half of the steak.
4. Spray the skillet with cooking spray, add onion and season with salt and pepper.
5. Cook 1 minute, then turn and cook the other side until onions are golden.
6. Lower heat to medium and add ½ tsp. olive oil to the skillet.
7. Add mushrooms, season with salt and pepper. Then lightly spray the mushrooms with cooking spray.
8. Cook 1 ½ minutes, then turn and cook for another 1 ½ minutes.
9. Add with steak and onions and serve.

Nutrition Information Per Serving

- Calories : 95.4
- Total fat : 4.1g
- Carbohydrate : 3.5g
- Protein : 12.5g

One Week Paleo Meal Plan

	Breakfast	Lunch	Diner
Monday	Omelet with Avocado and Pico De Gall	Sloppy Joe Baked Sweet Potatoes	Garlic Shrimp with Tomatoes
Tuesday	Turkey Sausage Breakfast Patties	Cauliflower Soup with Roasted Brussels Sprouts	Thai Coconut Shrimp Curry
Wednesday	Sweet Potato Chicken Hash with Eggs	Turkey Taco Lettuce Wraps	Spiced Flounder with Tomatoes
Thursday	Baked Eggs with Wilted Baby Spinach	Canned Tuna Ceviche	Beef, Cabbage, and Tomato Soup
Friday	Pumpkin Pie Oatmeal Breakfast Brûlée	California Grilled Chicken with Vinaigrette Dressing	Cuban Picadillo
Saturday	Baked Eggs in Harissa Spice	Blueberry Chicken Salad	Steak with Tomatoes
Sunday	Breakfast Muffins	Steak Kebabs with Chimichurri	Skillet Steak with Mushrooms and Onions

The Paleo diet includes real, whole foods and gives you an opportunity to eat healthily and lose weight. Despite the criticisms, if you follow the diet strictly you will lose body fat and feel more energetic and healthy. **Start the diet today!**

PALEO DIET 3 MONTH FOOD JORNAL

Date:	Dairy	Fruit	Grains	Proteins	Vegetables	Other

	Dairy	Fruit	Grains	Proteins	Vegetables	Other
Fresh salad					+	
Steak with tomatoes and rice			+	+	+	

Date:	Dairy	Fruit	Grains	Proteins	Vegetables	Other

Date:	Dairy	Fruit	Grains	Proteins	Vegetables	Other

Date:	Dairy	Fruit	Grains	Proteins	Vegetables	Other

Date:	Dairy	Fruit	Grains	Proteins	Vegetables	Other

Date:	Dairy	Fruit	Grains	Proteins	Vegetables	Other

Date:	Dairy	Fruit	Grains	Proteins	Vegetables	Other

Date:	Dairy	Fruit	Grains	Proteins	Vegetables	Other

Date:	Dairy	Fruit	Grains	Proteins	Vegetables	Other

Date:	Dairy	Fruit	Grains	Proteins	Vegetables	Other

Date:	Dairy	Fruit	Grains	Proteins	Vegetables	Other

Date:	Dairy	Fruit	Grains	Proteins	Vegetables	Other

Date:	Dairy	Fruit	Grains	Proteins	Vegetables	Other

Date:	Dairy	Fruit	Grains	Proteins	Vegetables	Other

	Dairy	Fruit	Grains	Proteins	Vegetables	Other
Date:						

	Dairy	Fruit	Grains	Proteins	Vegetables	Other

Date:	Dairy	Fruit	Grains	Proteins	Vegetables	Other

Date:	Dairy	Fruit	Grains	Proteins	Vegetables	Other

Date:	Dairy	Fruit	Grains	Proteins	Vegetables	Other

Date:	Dairy	Fruit	Grains	Proteins	Vegetables	Other

Date:	Dairy	Fruit	Grains	Proteins	Vegetables	Other

Date:	Dairy	Fruit	Grains	Proteins	Vegetables	Other

Date:	Dairy	Fruit	Grains	Proteins	Vegetables	Other

Date:	Dairy	Fruit	Grains	Proteins	Vegetables	Other

Date:	Dairy	Fruit	Grains	Proteins	Vegetables	Other

Date:	Dairy	Fruit	Grains	Proteins	Vegetables	Other

Date:	Dairy	Fruit	Grains	Proteins	Vegetables	Other

Date:	Dairy	Fruit	Grains	Proteins	Vegetables	Other

Date:	Dairy	Fruit	Grains	Proteins	Vegetables	Other

Date:	Dairy	Fruit	Grains	Proteins	Vegetables	Other

Date:	Dairy	Fruit	Grains	Proteins	Vegetables	Other

Date:	Dairy	Fruit	Grains	Proteins	Vegetables	Other

Date:	Dairy	Fruit	Grains	Proteins	Vegetables	Other

Date:	Dairy	Fruit	Grains	Proteins	Vegetables	Other

Date:	Dairy	Fruit	Grains	Proteins	Vegetables	Other

Date:	Dairy	Fruit	Grains	Proteins	Vegetables	Other

Date:	Dairy	Fruit	Grains	Proteins	Vegetables	Other

Date:	Dairy	Fruit	Grains	Proteins	Vegetables	Other

Date:	Dairy	Fruit	Grains	Proteins	Vegetables	Other

Date:	Dairy	Fruit	Grains	Proteins	Vegetables	Other

Date:	Dairy	Fruit	Grains	Proteins	Vegetables	Other

Date:	Dairy	Fruit	Grains	Proteins	Vegetables	Other

Date:	Dairy	Fruit	Grains	Proteins	Vegetables	Other

Date:	Dairy	Fruit	Grains	Proteins	Vegetables	Other

Date:	Dairy	Fruit	Grains	Proteins	Vegetables	Other

Date:	Dairy	Fruit	Grains	Proteins	Vegetables	Other

Date:	Dairy	Fruit	Grains	Proteins	Vegetables	Other

Date:	Dairy	Fruit	Grains	Proteins	Vegetables	Other

Date:	Dairy	Fruit	Grains	Proteins	Vegetables	Other

Date:	Dairy	Fruit	Grains	Proteins	Vegetables	Other

Date:	Dairy	Fruit	Grains	Proteins	Vegetables	Other

Date:	Dairy	Fruit	Grains	Proteins	Vegetables	Other

Date:	Dairy	Fruit	Grains	Proteins	Vegetables	Other

Date:	Dairy	Fruit	Grains	Proteins	Vegetables	Other

Date:	Dairy	Fruit	Grains	Proteins	Vegetables	Other

Date:	Dairy	Fruit	Grains	Proteins	Vegetables	Other

Date:	Dairy	Fruit	Grains	Proteins	Vegetables	Other

Date:	Dairy	Fruit	Grains	Proteins	Vegetables	Other

Date:	Dairy	Fruit	Grains	Proteins	Vegetables	Other

Date:	Dairy	Fruit	Grains	Proteins	Vegetables	Other

Date:	Dairy	Fruit	Grains	Proteins	Vegetables	Other

Date:	Dairy	Fruit	Grains	Proteins	Vegetables	Other

Date:	Dairy	Fruit	Grains	Proteins	Vegetables	Other

Date:	Dairy	Fruit	Grains	Proteins	Vegetables	Other

Date:	Dairy	Fruit	Grains	Proteins	Vegetables	Other

Date:	Dairy	Fruit	Grains	Proteins	Vegetables	Other

Date:	Dairy	Fruit	Grains	Proteins	Vegetables	Other

Date:	Dairy	Fruit	Grains	Proteins	Vegetables	Other

Date:	Dairy	Fruit	Grains	Proteins	Vegetables	Other

Date:	Dairy	Fruit	Grains	Proteins	Vegetables	Other

Date:	Dairy	Fruit	Grains	Proteins	Vegetables	Other

Date:	Dairy	Fruit	Grains	Proteins	Vegetables	Other

Date:	Dairy	Fruit	Grains	Proteins	Vegetables	Other

Date:	Dairy	Fruit	Grains	Proteins	Vegetables	Other

Date:	Dairy	Fruit	Grains	Proteins	Vegetables	Other

Date:	Dairy	Fruit	Grains	Proteins	Vegetables	Other

Date:	Dairy	Fruit	Grains	Proteins	Vegetables	Other

Date:	Dairy	Fruit	Grains	Proteins	Vegetables	Other

Date:	Dairy	Fruit	Grains	Proteins	Vegetables	Other

Date:	Dairy	Fruit	Grains	Proteins	Vegetables	Other

Date:	Dairy	Fruit	Grains	Proteins	Vegetables	Other

Date:	Dairy	Fruit	Grains	Proteins	Vegetables	Other

Date:	Dairy	Fruit	Grains	Proteins	Vegetables	Other

Date:	Dairy	Fruit	Grains	Proteins	Vegetables	Other

Date:	Dairy	Fruit	Grains	Proteins	Vegetables	Other

Date:	Dairy	Fruit	Grains	Proteins	Vegetables	Other

Date:	Dairy	Fruit	Grains	Proteins	Vegetables	Other

Date:	Dairy	Fruit	Grains	Proteins	Vegetables	Other

Date:	Dairy	Fruit	Grains	Proteins	Vegetables	Other

Date:	Dairy	Fruit	Grains	Proteins	Vegetables	Other

Date:	Dairy	Fruit	Grains	Proteins	Vegetables	Other

Date:	Dairy	Fruit	Grains	Proteins	Vegetables	Other

Date:	Dairy	Fruit	Grains	Proteins	Vegetables	Other

Date:	Dairy	Fruit	Grains	Proteins	Vegetables	Other

Date:	Dairy	Fruit	Grains	Proteins	Vegetables	Other

BONUS: SHOPPING LIST

SHOPPING LIST

FULL PROOF PALEO

FAT SOURCES

Best: Monosaturated Fats

- Avocado
- Avocado oil
- Hazelnuts / Filberts
- Macadamia nuts
- Macadamia oil
- Olives

Best: Saturated Fats

- Animal fats
- Clarified butter
- Coconut oil
- Coconut butter
- Coconut flakes
- Coconut milk

Occasional: Poly Fat

- Almonds / Almonds butter
- Brazil nuts
- Cashews / Cashews butter
- Pecans
- Pistachios

FRUITS

- Apples
- Apricots
- Bananas
- Blackberries
- Blueberries
- Cherries
- Date / Figs
- Exotic fruits
- Grapefruit
- Grapes
- Kiwi
- Lemon / Lime
- Mango
- Nectarines
- Oranges
- Papaya
- Peaches
- Pears
- Pineapple
- Plum
- Pomegranate
- Raspberries
- Strawberries
- Watermelon

VEGGIES

- Alfalfa sprouts
- Annise / Fennel root
- Artichoke
- Arugula
- Asparagus
- Beets
- Bok choy
- Broccoli
- Brussel sprouts
- Cauliflower
- Napa cabbage
- Carrots
- Celery
- Cucumber
- Eggplant
- Garlic
- Green Beans
- Greens
- Jicama
- Kale
- Kohlrabi
- Lettuce
- Mushrooms
- Onions

PROTEIN

- Eggs / Egg whites
  Best "Pasteurized + Organic"
  Fair "Organic"
  Acceptable "Store Bought"

- Poultry
  Chicken / Turkey / Game Birds

- Beef / Bison / Buffalo
- Other ruminants
  Lamb / Elk / Venison
- Other game meats
- Fish / Seafoods

- Pork

Download printability version:

http://foxsys.space/bonus/paleo-full.pdf